CGP punctuates your SATs prep with fun!

This Foundation SAT Buster from CGP is perfect for pupils who need some extra support in KS2 English — it's packed with simple Punctuation practice to build their skills towards the level of the SATs.

There's plenty of help along the way, with tips and model answers to help them get to grips with all the crucial skills.

We've also included fun self-assessment boxes to record how they're doing on each topic — and there's a handy scoresheet at the back!

What CGP is all about

Our sole aim here at CGP is to produce the highest quality books — carefully written, immaculately presented and dangerously close to being funny.

Then we work our socks off to get them out to you — at the cheapest possible prices.

Published by CGP

Editors: Izzy Bowen, Andy Cashmore, Robbie Driscoll, Catherine Heygate, Adam Worster

ISBN: 978 1 78908 427 6

With thanks to Amanda MacNaughton and James Summersgill for the proofreading.
Also thanks to Emily Smith for the copyright research.

Printed by Elanders Ltd, Newcastle upon Tyne.
Clipart from Corel®

Based on the classic CGP style created by Richard Parsons.

Contents

Section 1 – Basic Punctuation

Capital letters and full stops........................2
Exclamation marks and question marks 4
Sentences......................................6
Mixed practice................................10

Section 2 – Apostrophes and Inverted Commas

Apostrophes 12
Inverted commas 16
Mixed practice 20

Section 3 – Commas

Commas 22
Mixed practice 26

Section 4 – Brackets, Dashes and Hyphens

Brackets for extra information....................28
Dashes for extra information 30
Single dashes and bullet points.................31
Hyphens 32
Mixed practice 34

Section 5 – Colons and Semi-Colons

Colons 36
Semi-colons.................................38
Mixed practice 40

Section 6 – Mixed Practice

Mixed practice 42
Proofreading...............................45

Glossary 47
Scoresheet 48

Here's what you have to do...

In Year 6, you have to take some tests called the SATs.
This book will help you do well in the punctuation bit of the tests.

This is a Punctuation Python — it can punctuate even the trickiest sentences.

Your aim is to become a Punctuation Python.

Work through the questions in the book. When you come to a box like this, put a tick to show how you got on.

 If you got a lot of punctuation wrong, put a tick in the circle on the left. Don't worry — every Punctuation Python has to start somewhere. Make sure you know your punctuation rules inside out, then have another go.

If you're happy with some punctuation questions but still got a few wrong, put a tick in the middle circle. Ask your teacher to help you work out the areas you need more practice on.

  If you felt really confident and got nearly all the punctuation right, tick the circle on the right.

Congratulations — you're a Punctuation Python!

Punctuation Hints and Tips

The tips on this page may come in handy if you're having a punctuation problem.

1. Always use **capital letters** for proper nouns and after **full stops**, **exclamation marks** and **question marks**.

   Proper noun

   Whose dog is that**?** **I**t belongs to **L**ola. **W**hat a long dog it is**!**

   Capital letter   *Question mark*   *Full stop*   *Exclamation mark*

2. **Apostrophes** show that words have been **joined together**, or that something **belongs** to someone.

   John**'**s pudding.
   *This is to show **possession**.*

   We**'**ll meet you there.
   *This is a **contraction**, or **contracted form**, of 'we will'.*

3. Use **inverted commas** and **brackets** in **pairs**.

   "Why were you late?**"** Mrs Patel **(**my teacher**)** asked me.

4. **Commas** and **semi-colons** separate items in **lists**.

   I have a rabbit**,** five chickens**,** two goats and three gerbils. ← *Use commas for lists of shorter items.*

   I wore a purple hat, which I borrowed from Farai**;** a long woolly scarf, which is really cosy**;** and my favourite gloves. ← *Use semi-colons for lists of longer items, when commas would be confusing.*

5. **Commas** and **semi-colons** can also be used to **join related sentences**.

   I was hungry**;** I made myself a sandwich. ← *If you're using a semi-colon, the two sentences must make sense on their own.*

   I was hungry**, so** I made myself a sandwich. ← *If you join sentences with a comma, you need a joining word as well.*

6. **Colons** introduce **lists** or **join sentences** (when the second sentence **explains** the first).

   I have three hobbies**:** reading, basketball and painting. ← *The bit before the colon must make sense on its own.*

   We need to tidy up**:** Mum will be home in five minutes. ←

Capital letters and full stops

> **Warm Up**
>
> *Answer this question for some practice on when to use capital letters.*
>
> 1) There is one mistake in the use of capital letters in each of the sentences below. Circle the letters that should be capital letters.
>
> **there's no chocolate left in the fridge.**
>
> **We went to see the new show on saturday.**
>
> **Leia and i spent all afternoon in the garden.**

Now try these questions to practise using capital letters and full stops.

2) Put a tick next to the words which should always start with a capital letter.

britain ☐	banana ☐	january ☐
green ☐	tennis ☐	jennifer ☐

——————
2 marks

3) Rewrite these sentences, adding capital letters where they are needed.

elliot played chess with mrs shadid on tuesday.

...Elliot played chess with Mrs Shadid on Tuesday.............................

sometimes, i go to london on the train.

....

on friday, you have a meeting with dr jones.

....

i haven't seen olivia since november.

——————
....
2 marks

Capital letters and full stops

4) There should be **four** full stops in this paragraph, but they're all missing.
Circle the **four** words which should have a full stop after them.

> The first person to travel to space was a man called Yuri Gagarin
> He first trained as a pilot and then as an astronaut On 12th April
> 1961, Yuri flew into space, travelled once around Earth and then
> landed safely back home His journey lasted just under two hours

2 marks

5) Read these sentences. Tick the **two** sentences where capital letters and
full stops have been used correctly.

My uncle comes to visit us every Tuesday evening. ☐

It rained for all of august and most of september ☐

Tomorrow, i am going on Holiday to France. ☐

Mr Marchant couldn't wait for Solomon to arrive. ☐

2 marks

6) Write a sentence using each of the words below.
Add capital letters and full stops where they are needed.

Each sentence should be about something different.

spain: *The rain in Spain goes down the drain.*

thursday: ....

february: ....

lucy: ....

2 marks

*Punctuation Pythons know how to use capital letters
and full stops in the right places. Do you? Tick a box.*

Exclamation marks and question marks

Now have a go at these questions about both question marks and exclamation marks.

2) Draw a line to match the two parts of these sentences so that they make sense.

   Where did you   this film before?

   It's so good   that wall!

   Has anybody seen   out of my house!

   Look out for   put the treasure?

   Get that frog   to see you again!

   _____
   2 marks

3) Read these sentences. Tick the **two** sentences that use correct punctuation.

   Why are the walls green?   ☐

   Who is in charge here!   ☐

   Don't touch the kitten?   ☐   Use an exclamation mark to show strong emotion or to emphasise a point.

   Thank you so much!   ☐

   _____
   2 marks

Exclamation marks and question marks

4) Rearrange all of the words in the box to make a sentence. Then decide whether it needs a question mark or an exclamation mark at the end.

> you   hat   ~~What~~   today   lovely   are   wearing   a

.....What .... _____

1 mark

5) Write **four** questions, using the words below as a starting point.

What ....is your favourite TV show?..

Why ....

How ....

When ....

Where .... _____

2 marks

6) Complete each of these sentences with an exclamation mark or a question mark.

"Noor, come down for dinner ☐ " Mum shouted from the kitchen.

Why is that kangaroo wearing a jacket ☐

> Remember that 'What' and 'How' can begin both questions and exclamations.

Will you please stop eating my cakes ☐

What a crazy day it's been ☐ _____

2 marks

Punctuation Pythons are ace at exclamation marks and question marks, but are you? Tick one of the boxes.

Section 1 — Basic Punctuation

Sentences

Here's a warm up question about sentences to ease you in.

> A command is a sentence that tells somebody to do something.

1) Read these sentences. Put a 'Q' in each box after a question, and a 'C' in each box after a command.

Where has Julia gone? ☐   Put your socks on. ☐

Brush your teeth twice a day. ☐   How did I get here? ☐

Give me your hand. ☐   What's that smell? ☐

Now see how well you get on with some more questions about types of sentences.

2) Draw a line to show whether each sentence is a statement or a command.

Ostriches can run very quickly.

Asha fell asleep at once.

Come back here right now.

Take the rubbish outside.

Don't move a muscle.

I got a new bike for Christmas.

> A statement is a sentence that gives information.

statement

command

2 marks

3) Rearrange the words in the boxes to make a sentence. Circle the correct sentence type in bold to show if the sentence is a statement, a question or a command.

| snowman | a | The | . | nose | needs |

....

statement   **question**   **command**

2 marks

Sentences

4) Read these sentences. Tick the **three** sentences that are commands.

Take off your shoes when you come into the house. ☐

Why weren't you in school today? ☐

What a tasty pancake that was! ☐

Listen to what I'm telling you. ☐

Wait here for ten minutes. ☐

Fabian's dog ran to fetch the stick. ☐

2 marks

5) Write the question you would need to ask to get each of the answers below.
Use the correct punctuation.

My name is Joanna.

.....What is your name?...

Naomi went to the shops.

.....Where...

The party is on Saturday.

.....When..

Rhys won the race.

.....Who...

I used magic to defeat the dragon.

.....How...

2 marks

Sentences

6) In the boxes below, add a question mark to the sentences that are questions and an exclamation mark to the sentences that are exclamations.

What is the view like ⏍?⏍

What an amazing view that is ⏍!⏍

Why are you wearing that hat ☐

How strange you look in that hat ☐

What a large fish you've caught ☐

How large is the fish you caught ☐

> Exclamations always begin with either 'what' or 'how' and contain a verb. They usually have an exclamation mark at the end.

2 marks

7) Sort the sentences below under the correct headings in the table.
Write either a full stop or a question mark at the end of each sentence.

~~I like playing tennis~~   How are you   What's the matter

Who said that   Rico ate the apple   There's no jam

Statement	Question
I like playing tennis.	

2 marks

Sentences

8) Use each set of words to write a command.

| slowly | corridor | walk |

This is just an example. You could write any command as long as it uses all the words correctly.

......Walk slowly in the corridor...

| food | bus | eat |

...Don't...

| elbows | off | table |

....

| hide | crocodile | quickly |

....

2 marks

9) Read these pairs of sentences. Circle the version with the most suitable punctuation.

I couldn't sleep all night?	I couldn't sleep all night.
Stop right there!	Stop right there.
They walked slowly!	They walked slowly.
Run as fast as you can?	Run as fast as you can!

2 marks

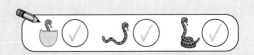

A Punctuation Python knows its commands from its statements, but what about you? Give yourself a tick.

Mixed practice

Warm Up

Here's a quick warm up question about capital letters.

1)   Circle the **six** letters in the paragraph below that should be capital letters.

Don't forget you need capital letters for days of the week, months of the year, people's names and 'I'.

> tommy plays basketball every thursday after school.
> in march, his team won a tournament against all
> the local schools. this means that they've qualified
> for a national tournament in manchester.

Now have a go at some more questions to test everything you learned in this section.

2)   The words in these sentences are all jumbled up. Rewrite each sentence in the correct order. Add capital letters and a full stop where they are needed.

| think | | is | | stacy | | we | | funny |

....

| hope | | i | | christmas | | it | | this | | snows |

....

2 marks

3)   Read these pairs of sentences. Put a tick next to the version with the most suitable punctuation.

| What did you say? | ☐ | What did you say. | ☐ |

| I can't see anything? | ☐ | I can't see anything! | ☐ |

| Rachel likes cornflakes. | ☐ | Rachel likes cornflakes? | ☐ |

2 marks

Mixed practice

4) Rearrange the words in each grey box to make a sentence.
    Then, in the white boxes, write whether each sentence
    is a statement (S), command (C) or question (Q).

| from | cats | ? | ~~Where~~ | these | did | come |

.....Where.. ☐

| every | Scott | . | badminton | plays | Saturday |

.... ☐

| going | ! | Watch | you | where | are |

.... ☐ _____

2 marks

5) Write whether each of these sentences is a statement, a question or a command.

Giraffes live in Africa.   ....statement.................

Have you seen Catriona?   ....

Abigail plays the guitar.   ....

Put that back right now!   ....

Write to me soon.   ....

When did you see Gran?   ....

2 marks

_Looks like you've slithered your way to the end of the
section. But how did you get on? Tick one of the boxes._

Section 1 — Basic Punctuation

Apostrophes

Warm Up

Test your knowledge of apostrophes with this warm up question.

A contraction, or a contracted form, is a shortened version of a phrase.

1)   Join up each set of words with the correct contraction.

I had	**I've**
is not	**it's**
will not	**I'd**
I have	**won't**
would not	**isn't**
it is	**wouldn't**

Now have a go at some more questions on apostrophes.

When you're writing contractions, the apostrophe should replace the missing letter(s) in each word. E.g. you are = you're.

2)   Circle the correct word in bold in each sentence.

I **ca'nt / can't** believe my goldfish won the race.

Bradley **should've / shouldv'e** known which shoes were his.

Daria wished she **hadn't / had'nt** reacted so angrily.

Jack knew **the'yd / they'd** be back.

_____
2 marks

3)   Tick the **two** sentences which use apostrophes correctly.

She's been out looking for koalas again.   ☐

They were'nt ready for so much rain.   ☐

There's no way I'm doing that.   ☐

I could'nt see anything in the dark room.   ☐

Look carefully at where the apostrophes have been put.

_____
2 marks

Apostrophes

4) Each of these sentences is missing an apostrophe. Tick the box above each sentence where the apostrophe should be added.

Apostrophes can show that something belongs to someone.

☐   ☐   ☐   ☐

Leonards mother adores horses.   Those socks are Amys.

☐   ☐   ☐   ☐

The jugs handle is made of glass.   A dogs life is full of mysteries.

_____
2 marks

5) Read these pairs of sentences. Put a tick next to the version that uses apostrophes correctly.

Ruby's gerbil is dangerous. ☐   Rubys' gerbil is dangerous. ☐

The milkmans' van is white. ☐   The milkman's van is white. ☐

My brothers feet smell. ☐   My brother's feet smell. ☐

_____
2 marks

6) For each pair of words, write a sentence using an apostrophe and the given words.

clown   nose

.....*The clown's nose was bright red.*...

runner   leg

....

castle   towers

....

_____
2 marks

Apostrophes

7) Tick the **two** sentences where the word in bold is plural.

The **astronauts'** rocket has landed. ☐

'Plural' means more than one.

The **girl's** legs hurt from walking. ☐

The **rabbit's** carrot was stuck in the ground. ☐

The **dancers'** pet donkey is very friendly. ☐

_____
2 marks

8) Draw a line to match each sentence to the phrase that means the same thing.

The bag that belongs to the teacher.	the teachers' bag
The bag that belongs to two teachers.	the teachers' bags
Two bags that belong to two teachers.	the teacher's bag

_____
2 marks

9) Write out the sentences below using apostrophes to show who owns what.

The table that belongs to the sisters. ....the sisters' table..........

The brush that belongs to the painter. ....

The chest that belongs to the pirates. ....

The grapes that belong to the king. ....

The eyes that belong to the aliens. ....

The bananas that belong to the monkey. ....

_____
2 marks

Apostrophes

10) Write the correct word to finish each sentence.

your / you're: I hope ......*you're*........ coming to visit soon.

If you're stuck, try changing the shortened version for the longer version — e.g. <u>you're</u> to <u>you are</u>.

your / you're: I really like .... dress today.

were / we're: Where .... you all this time?

were / we're: I think .... all feeling better.

their / they're: He forgot that .... both vegetarians.

their / they're: Have you seen .... new trampoline?

_____
2 marks

11) Draw a line to match each sentence with the correct form of its or it's.

.... time for some cake.

.... teeth are very sharp.

I know .... a difficult decision.

The dog wagged .... tail.

its

it's

Don't forget — <u>it's</u> means <u>it is</u> or <u>it has</u>, but <u>its</u> means <u>belongs to it</u>.

_____
2 marks

12) Fill in the blanks using words from the box.

| your | they're | you're | there |

" .... grandparents will be here soon," Mum told the children.

" .... coming to look after you while we're away, so make sure

.... nice to them or .... will be trouble when we're back."

_____
2 marks

Punctuation Pythons eat apostrophes for breakfast.
What about you? Tick to show which python you are.

     Section 2 — Apostrophes and Inverted Commas

Inverted commas

Warm Up

Inverted commas are also known as speech marks — they are used to show that someone is speaking. Try this warm up question to get you started.

1) One of the sentences below uses inverted commas correctly.
    Tick **one** box to show the sentence that is correct.

    "I've lost my llama, Charlie said." ☐

    "I've lost my llama, Charlie" said. ☐

    "I've lost my llama," Charlie said. ☐

Now make sure you really understand inverted commas by giving these questions a go.

2) Each of these sentences is missing a set of inverted commas.
    Put a set of inverted commas in **one** of the boxes to make each sentence correct.

    "What have you done with my toothbrush? ["] Max [ ] asked. ⬅ This one has been done for you.

    [ ] Mohammed said, [ ] That's a funny-looking palm tree."

    "Stop throwing cucumbers! [ ] Kieran cried [ ] .

    India said, [ ] I told you [ ] not to come in here."

    _____
    2 marks

3) Each of these sentences is missing either a comma or a full stop.
    Write the correct punctuation mark in each box.

    "I wish it would just stop raining," Mum said [ ]

    Kai asked the alien [ ] "Are you from Mars?"

    "Do not drink this potion," the wizard told me [ ]

    Tristan said [ ] "Those oranges are enormous."

    _____
    2 marks

Inverted commas

4) Read these pair of sentences. Put a tick next
    to the version that uses punctuation correctly.

"Who are you"? Priya asked. ☐   "Who are you?" Priya asked. ☐

Doug shouted, "I can't see!" ☐   Doug shouted, "I can't see"! ☐

"Hurry up," whispered Yasmin. ☐   "Hurry up." whispered Yasmin. ☐

"Someone help", Ronan cried. ☐   "Someone help!" Ronan cried. ☐

_____
2 marks

5) Rewrite these sentences, adding capital letters where they are needed.

the vet said, "your monkey thinks he's a rock star."

.....The vet said, "Your monkey thinks he's a rock star."...............

"what a lot of fuss!" cried the teacher.

....

lottie said, "this is the biggest room in the house."

....

"everyone likes trains," said james.

....
_____
2 marks

6) Use the words and punctuation marks in the box to make a new sentence.

| hat | said | Your | , | beautiful | . | " | ~~Amelie~~ | is | " |

.....Amelie...
_____
1 mark

Inverted commas

7) Read these pairs of sentences.
    Circle the sentences that contain direct speech.

Direct speech shows exactly what someone says and uses " ".

"I hate jelly," she said.	She said that she hated jelly.
I cried that I was hungry.	"I'm hungry!" I cried.
Barney said that I speak too quickly.	Barney said, "You speak too quickly."
"Follow the path," the goblin said.	The goblin said to follow the path.

2 marks

8) Read each sentence and tick the correct box to
    show if it is direct speech or reported speech.

Reported speech describes what someone has said, but not in their own words.

direct   reported

"Jenny's work has really improved," the teacher said.   ☑   ☐

They asked whether it was always this windy.   ☐   ☐

"Keep going! Just one more lap!" Mum shouted.   ☐   ☐

Paul said, "There's something in my teeth."   ☐   ☐

The scientist told us not to touch the dinosaur eggs.   ☐   ☐

2 marks

9) These sentences are all in reported speech.
    Rewrite them so that they use direct speech.

Don't forget to use a capital letter at the start of direct speech.

Pablo said that the rocket won't fly.

.....**"The rocket** ....

Gran asked me how tall I am.

.....**Gran asked,** ....

2 marks

Inverted commas

10) Use the words in each box to write a sentence using direct speech.

said	juggling	clown	bored

Make sure you use inverted commas in both sentences.

....

....

station	asked	Nicole	where

....

....

_____
2 marks

11) Read the text in the grey box. Change each line of reported speech to a line of direct speech by filling in the gaps below.

Don't forget to add the correct punctuation marks.

> Axel asked Ruth if she had seen the talking tree.
> Ruth said that trees can't talk.
> Axel cried that this tree could talk.
> The tree said that it wasn't an ordinary tree.

"Have you seen .... Axel asked Ruth.

"Tree's can't ....

"This tree .... Axel cried.

.... the tree said.

_____
2 marks

Punctuation Pythons are experts at inverted commas, but how well do you understand them? Tick a box.

Mixed practice

> ### Warm Up
>
> *Here's a quick question to help you recap what you've learned about apostrophes.*
>
> 1) Tick the **two** sentences where the word in bold is singular.
>
> My **uncle's** farm is near here. ☐
>
> The **trolls'** heads were green and spotty. ☐
>
> The **town's** buildings are made of stone. ☐
>
> Those are the **hikers'** tents. ☐
>
> *Singular means there's only one.*

Now try these questions about both apostrophes and inverted commas.

2) Complete these sentences using the contracted forms of the words in brackets.

The cat ....<u>can't</u>........ (**can not**) get down from the tree.

We .... (**should have**) arrived hours ago.

The baby .... (**will not**) stop climbing on the dog.

I don't think .... (**they are**) going to the disco.

It .... (**is not**) safe to play here.

I .... (**have not**) heard of that film.

_____
2 marks

3) Write a sentence using direct speech which includes the words in the boxes below.

Make sure you use inverted commas in your sentence.

| said | they're | their |

....

....

_____
1 mark

Mixed practice

4) These sentences are missing some bits of punctuation.
In each box, write either an apostrophe or a set of inverted commas.

"My brothers ☐ noses are all very long, ☐ I explained.

☐ I would love to meet the tooth fairy! ☐ Robin cried.

☐ The ants ☐ nest has grown again," Dad said.

Farah ☐ s aunt said that she couldn ☐ t come on Wednesday.

_____
2 marks

5) Read the passage. Rewrite the conversation in direct speech.

> Timothy asked Laura if she had a good birthday.
> Laura said that she had a great birthday.
> Timothy asked her what her favourite present was.
> Laura said her favourite present was definitely the unicycle.

Tackle this question one line at a time.

"Did you have a good birthday, Laura?" Timothy asked. ....

....

....

....

....

....

_____
2 marks

Wow, that section wasn't easy. Did you manage to crack it like a true Punctuation Python? Tick one of the boxes.

Commas

Warm Up

Test what you know about commas by answering this question.

1) One of the sentences below uses commas correctly.
Tick **one** box to show the sentence that is correct.

To go, skiing you need a coat two skis and, a sense of adventure. ☐

The petting zoo only had sheep, goats and badgers. ☐

Tabby's favourite sports were, tennis, cricket, and skydiving. ☐

Now try these questions to practise using commas.

2) Each of these sentences is missing a comma.
Put a comma in **one** of the boxes to make each sentence correct.

I felt like eating either a burger ☐ a sandwich or ☐ a hotdog.

I would like to ☐ visit France ☐ Egypt and Spain.

We went ☐ to the ice rink ☐ the cinema and the ☐ zoo.

_____
2 marks

3) Rewrite these sentences, adding commas where they are needed.

Leanne Freddie and Ruby are triplets.

....

Imogen found two shoes a spoon and a can.

....

You need eggs flour butter and sugar for the cake. ⬅ *This sentence needs more than one comma because there are more than three things in the list.*

....

....

_____
2 marks

Commas

4) Finish the sentences below with the names of Fi's cats and dogs.
Remember to add commas in the right places.

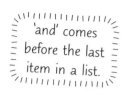
'and' comes before the last item in a list.

Fi's cats: Treacle   Ginger   Fifi   Socks
Fi's dogs: Bella   Old Rover   Cuddles   Max

Fi's cats are called ....

Fi's dogs are called ....
_____
2 marks

5) Tick the **three** sentences that use commas correctly.

Before lunch we played, outside.   ☐

At the bottom, of the sea there are many unusual creatures.   ☐

Afterwards, we'll drop Fahad off at his martial arts class.   ☐

When I'm tired, I get grumpy.   ☐

While we watched, the film we ate some pizza.   ☐

Next to the table, there was a giraffe.   ☐
_____
2 marks

6) Each of these sentences has a comma that isn't needed.
Cross out the comma that isn't needed in each sentence.

During dinner, I noticed a strange smell coming, from upstairs.

When the film started, everyone stopped, talking.

Although it was dark, outside, she didn't bring a torch.
_____
2 marks

Commas

7) Rewrite these sentences so that each one starts with the underlined adverbial.

Our picnic was ruined <u>because of the rain</u>.

..........Because of the rain, our picnic was ruined..................

You will find a secret door <u>under the bridge</u>.

....

Connie becomes invisible <u>every Thursday</u>.

....

2 marks

8) Each box below contains a sentence that has been jumbled up.
Draw a line from the beginning of each sentence to the end, going
through the punctuation marks in the right places.

Amina found a strange book

, , .

Last Saturday   which had belonged to her mum

When we finished sailing

. , ,

which was by the bank   we went to the cafe

2 marks

9) Join up each sentence (in a white box) with its meaning (in a grey box).

Do you know Marc?   Asking Marc if he knows something.

Do you know, Marc?   Asking someone if they know Marc.

1 mark

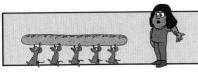

Commas

10) Read this passage.

> Alice likes painting animals. She also likes judo. She also likes poetry.

Add **one** comma to the sentence below
so it matches the meaning of the passage.

Alice is interested in painting animals judo and poetry.

_____
1 mark

11) Rewrite each sentence, using a pair of commas
to add the words in the box in the right place.

The scientists found a cure.   who had done lots of research

...The scientists, who had done lots of research, found a cure.............

My uncle can juggle.   who was in the circus

....

The old pot broke.   which was made of glass

....
_____
2 marks

12) Add commas to separate the extra information in each sentence.

The liquid which was green tasted strange.

Lewis who is always late missed the bus again.

My aunt who lives in Scotland came to visit.

My favourite shirt which I wear all the time has disappeared.

> If you take away all the words separated by the commas, the sentence should still make sense.

_____
2 marks

Punctuation Pythons can gulp down commas whole.
How did you find these pages? Tick one of the boxes.

Section 3 — Commas

Mixed practice

Make sure you're comfortable with commas by answering this question...

1) Tick the **two** sentences that use commas correctly.

   After the film, we went bowling. ☐

   You need to add, broccoli carrots and cream. ☐

   While I was, sleeping it started to snow. ☐

   Zak enjoys swimming, karate and playing chess. ☐

Test everything you've learned about commas by trying these questions.

2) Read the sentence below. Circle the reason commas have been used.

   The old man, who lived in a stone cottage, walked down the lane.

Commas are used to separate items in a list.	**Commas are used to separate extra information.**

   _____
   1 mark

3) For each sentence below, write in the box whether
   0, 1 or 2 commas should be added.

   I need a new T-shirt and some trainers. ☐

   Our school project which is on reptiles is almost finished. ☐

   Under the desk the little cat trembled with fear. ☐

   The spaceship landed in the field at the end of the lane. ☐

   The beach shop sells postcards sunglasses and sandals. ☐

   _____
   2 marks

Mixed practice

4) Each sentence below has a comma missing. Add **one** comma to each sentence.

After our holiday my sister made a scrapbook of the trip.

London, Birmingham Manchester and Glasgow are all cities.

In the orchard, there was an apple tree a pear tree and some flowers.

When I get home I'm going to have a nap.

_____
2 marks

5) This sentence is missing some words. Add words of your own so that the sentence makes sense and is punctuated correctly.

The doll, ..which...,

is ....old......... , ... and ....

_____
2 marks

6) Use the words in each set of boxes to write a sentence.
Each sentence needs **two** commas.

| which was black and white | came home | ~~the missing cat~~ |

..The missing cat,...

....

| burst into flames | the tablecloth | which was brand new |

....

....

_____
2 marks

Section 3 — Commas

Brackets for extra information

Here's a warm up question on brackets to get you started.

1) Tick the **one** sentence that uses brackets correctly.

   My local football team is (Boottown FC). ☐

   (The alien) was wearing high heels. ☐

   Over half (the town was watching. ☐

   I look like my grandma (my mum's mum). ☐

   > Brackets go around extra information in a sentence. The extra information is called a parenthesis.

Now you've done the warm up, make a start on these questions.

2) Each of these sentences is missing a pair of brackets. Rewrite each sentence, adding a pair of brackets.

   Turnips a kind of root vegetable are my favourite food.

   > If you take away all the words in the brackets, the sentence should still make sense.

   ...Turnips (a kind of root vegetable) are my favourite food.......................

   My two cousins Ewan and Leah really like robots.

   ....

   Everyone played Snap a type of card game.

   ....

   _____
   2 marks

3) Write a sentence using the words in the box and one more bracket.

   | friendly | baker | is | ~~the~~ | ~~Mr Crumbs~~ | very | village |

   ...Mr Crumbs (the...

   ....

   _____
   1 mark

Brackets for extra information

4) Each of these sentences only has one bracket.
Put the other bracket in the correct box.

Owls and bats are both nocturnal (they are active ☐ at night ☐ .

She lived in Poland ☐ for a long time ☐ over twelve years).

Scamp ☐ my uncle's ☐ dog) is a golden retriever.

We went to France (a country in Europe ☐ for our holiday ☐ .

2 marks

5) Rewrite each sentence, using a pair of brackets
to add the words in the box in the right place.

Cheese and treacle sandwiches are easy to make. | my favourite snack |

...Cheese and treacle sandwiches (my favourite snack) are easy to make....

Two people are off sick today. | Bella and Katie |

....

Use the map to get home. | the magic one |

....

2 marks

6) Write something in the gaps between the brackets to complete these sentences.

Buckingham Palace (......where the Queen lives......) is in London.

Dr Norton (..) is always busy.

We let Snowball (..) out of her cage.

2 marks

Punctuation Pythons are bracket experts, but how happy
are you with them? Tick one of the boxes (on the right).

© CGP — not to be photocopied   *Section 4 — Brackets, Dashes and Hyphens*

Dashes for extra information

Warm Up

You can also add a parenthesis (extra information) to a sentence with a pair of dashes.

1) The box below contains a sentence that's been jumbled up.
Draw a line from the beginning of the sentence to the end,
going through the punctuation marks in the right places.

> which she brings everywhere
>
> **!**   ⊝
>
> isn't even waterproof   ⊝   Granny's umbrella

Work through these questions about using dashes to add extra information.

2) Each of these sentences should have two dashes, but there is only one.
Put the other dash in the correct box.

The old man ☐ he must have been ☐ over ninety — was shouting wildly.

Partridge Lane — the street ☐ where I was born ☐ is not far from here.

That girl ☐ in the photo — the really tall one ☐ is my friend Jasmine.

_____
2 marks

3) Rewrite these sentences, adding two dashes
to each sentence to separate the extra information.

The mayor a friendly woman gave a speech.

....

My party which is next week will be great.

....

_____
2 marks

Punctuation Pythons may not have legs, but they sure
know how to dash. Do you? Tick one of the boxes.

Single dashes and bullet points

Warm Up

Dashes can also be used on their own. Try this warm up question on single dashes.

1) In each of the sentences below, only one of the dashes is needed.
Cross out the dash that isn't needed in each sentence.

I can't wait for Christmas — the whole family — is coming to stay.

We all saw — the alien spaceship — it landed on the school field.

Pat had to go — home because she's ill — she's the third person this week.

Now get stuck into these questions on single dashes and bullet points.

2) Each sentence is missing a dash. Put a dash in the correct box.

My mum looked silly ☐ she'd forgotten ☐ to put her shoes on.

Mount Everest is ☐ 8 848m tall ☐ it's the highest mountain in the world.

Josh got to take ☐ the class hamster home ☐ I was very jealous.

2 marks

3) Below is a list of things that Jing should do on her holiday.
Write out the list using bullet points.

On her holiday, Jing should go to the beach, visit a museum and go shopping.

On her holiday, Jing should do these things:

Start each bullet point with a capital letter to be consistent.

• Go to the beach

....

....

....

1 mark

Were you as brilliant at this page as a Punctuation Python would be? Tick a box to show how confident you are.

Hyphens

Hyphens bring together two words, or two parts of a word. Have a go at this question.

1) Tick the version of each sentence which uses hyphens correctly.

I can see twenty-three birds. ☐ I can see twenty three-birds. ☐

He is a scary looking-clown. ☐ He is a scary-looking clown. ☐

This is a half-finished book. ☐ This is a half finished-book. ☐

Keep going with some more questions on hyphens.

2) Draw lines to match each phrase with the correct definition.

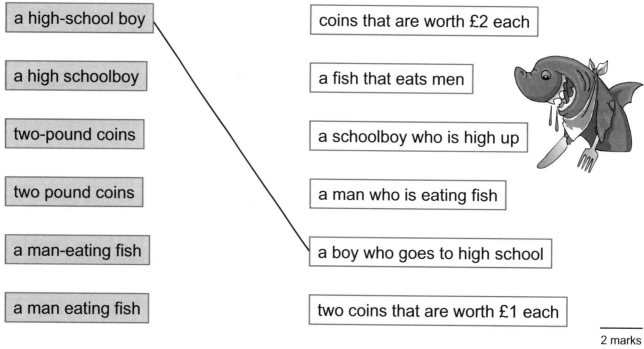

a high-school boy

a high schoolboy

two-pound coins

two pound coins

a man-eating fish

a man eating fish

coins that are worth £2 each

a fish that eats men

a schoolboy who is high up

a man who is eating fish

a boy who goes to high school

two coins that are worth £1 each

2 marks

3) Only one of the hyphens is needed in the sentence below.
Cross out all of the hyphens that aren't needed.

The luxury-mansion had four-tennis courts and an open-air swimming pool.

1 mark

Hyphens

4) Underline the word in the last two columns that best fits the description in the first column.

The prefix 're' plus a hyphen means 'to do something again'.

take something off	<u>remove</u>	re-move
sign something again	resign	re-sign
answer someone	reply	re-ply
solve something again	resolve	re-solve
cover something again	recover	re-cover
investigate something	research	re-search

2 marks

5) Each sentence below is missing **one** hyphen.
Rewrite each sentence with the hyphen in the correct place.

Amanda loved working in her family owned cafe.

Amanda loved working in her family-owned cafe.

I live on a very narrow one way street.

....

There are sixty seven plums in the fridge.

....

We found a funny smelling box outside our door.

....

2 marks

Phew! That was a tough topic. Did you unleash your inner python and figure it all out? Tick one of the boxes.

Section 4 — Brackets, Dashes and Hyphens

Mixed practice

Try your hand at this question for a reminder of how single dashes work.

1) Tick the **two** sentences that use dashes correctly.

I read that book — last week it was great. ☐

That house is scary — they say it's haunted. ☐

David has a piano — concert he's nervous about. ☐

Hiba loves tennis — she plays it all the time. ☐

Make sure you understand the whole section with this jumble of questions.

2) Add a pair of brackets to each of these sentences so they are punctuated correctly.

The snowman the one in the garden has frozen in place.

Ben Deelegs a famous gymnast visited our school.

The girl at the back she's called Steph wouldn't stop talking.

A heavy book a large dictionary fell off the shelf with a thud.

_____
2 marks

3) Below is a list of things that Peter needs to buy.
Write out the list using bullet points.

Peter needs to buy a telescope, three potted plants and a pair of gloves.

Peter needs to buy these things:

....

....

....

_____
1 mark

Mixed practice

4) Write whether a hyphen or a dash should complete each sentence below.

Chloe didn't finish her drink .. I saw her throw it away. ....dash.............

The leather .. bound book is expensive. ....

The robot was broken .. its arms fell off. ....

The show was very funny .. we couldn't stop laughing. ....

The magician's spell had long .. term effects. ....

2 marks

5) Rewrite this sentence, adding a hyphen where it is needed.

Larry arrived riding a friendly looking mammoth.

....

....

1 mark

6) Write something in each gap to complete the sentence.

This is just an example — you could write anything in this gap that makes sense.

Kymani's favourite restaurant — ....which is opposite his house........ — is called 'The Dino Diner'.

The man in the car — .... — looks very suspicious to me.

Molly's ice cream — .... — had melted.

Susie's coat — .... — was missing.

2 marks

That's the end of the section. Did you ace these pages like a true Punctuation Python? Tick one of the boxes.

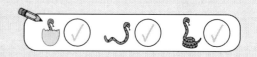

Section 4 — Brackets, Dashes and Hyphens

Colons

Warm Up

Time for a warm up question about colons.

1)   Tick the **two** sentences that use colons correctly.

> *The bit before the colon must make sense on its own.*

I like: pop music, rock music and jazz.   ☐

They sell cars in four different colours: red, blue, white and pink.   ☐

I'd like to see these people: William, Karim, Florence and Eva.   ☐

There were three cakes, a fairy cake: a sponge cake and a tart.   ☐

The questions on the next two pages are all about colons. Time to get to it...

2)   The box below contains three sentences that are jumbled up. Draw a line from the beginning of each sentence to the end, going through the colon in the right place.

> *When a colon introduces an explanation, the bit of the sentence after the colon explains the bit before it.*

Tajus needs a new watch	Ada went to bed	The chair was wobbly
⦂	⦂	⦂
one of the legs was broken.	he lost his old one.	she had a headache.

2 marks

3)   Put colons in the correct places so that these sentences make sense.

There were only three animals ☐ in the zoo ☐ a tiger, a giraffe and a lion.

I've lived in three different cities ☐ Liverpool, London ☐ and Cardiff.

Sam did ballet three times ☐ a week ☐ on Mondays, Fridays and Sundays.

There were just five ☐ people ☐ two doctors, two teachers and a priest.

2 marks

Colons

4) Rewrite each sentence, adding a colon in the correct place.

I couldn't believe my eyes the goose was reading a newspaper.

I couldn't believe my eyes: the goose was reading a newspaper.

Sanjay was tired he'd been travelling all day.

....

Ella wasn't at home she had gone to the cinema.

....

You should know something I snore really loudly.

....

2 marks

5) Tick the **three** sentences that use a colon correctly.

I watched TV: Ben ate some crisps. ☐

People were getting impatient: the queue was long. ☐

I saw: five children, two adults and a hippo. ☐

You need to bring these things: a pencil, a hat and a coat. ☐

Paula was very cold: she'd forgotten to bring a coat. ☐

He can play the guitar: she can play the piano. ☐

2 marks

For Punctuation Pythons, colons are a piece of snake.
Tick a box to show what kind of python you are.

Section 5 — Colons and Semi-Colons

Semi-colons

Warm Up

The semi-colon is the last punctuation mark that you need to know (phew!)
Semi-colons are used to join two main clauses or to separate items in a list...

1) Circle the **two** sentences where the underlined
   conjunction could be replaced with a semi-colon.

   He regretted his choice <u>but</u> it   The monster was completely
   was too late to change his mind.   green <u>and</u> smelled of fish.

   My favourite show is on   Jakub played in the park <u>while</u>
   tonight <u>after</u> the evening news.   his mum sat on a bench.

See how you get on with some more questions on semi-colons.

2) Tick the **two** sentences where semi-colons have been used correctly.

   I visited Gran; and brought her some flowers. ☐

   They were late again; they had no excuse. ☐

   Frankie had a pet duck; she took it for walks. ☐

   The parachute is in the box; under the stairs. ☐

   Only use semi-colons to join together two complete sentences.

   _____
   2 marks

3) Put semi-colons in the correct boxes so that these sentences make sense.

   Erin plays squash on Wednesdays ☐ she loves ☐ playing sports.

   He moved to the countryside ☐ he prefers ☐ it because it's quieter.

   British people call them ☐ trousers ☐ Americans call them pants.

   Come back tomorrow ☐ we might ☐ be less busy then.

   _____
   2 marks

4) Add semi-colons where they are needed in the second list.
    The first list has been done for you.

If you use semi-colons to separate the items in a list, you need to have one before the 'and'.

> I hardly recognised Maja : she was wearing her mum's high heels ; her face was covered in lipstick , which was bright purple ; and she had put on her dad's glasses.

> The only flavours they have left are chocolate , which I've already tried strawberry , which is my favourite and a little bit of vanilla.

1 mark

5) Rewrite these sentences, adding semi-colons where they are needed.

    It was beginning to get misty we struggled to see each other.

    It was beginning to get misty; we struggled to see each other.

    They always cheat I won't play with them.

    ....

    The model was made from long, thin pieces
    of wood plastic pots and lots of glue.

    ....

    ....

    Whenever I go camping, I always bring my tent
    a coat, in case it rains and my red backpack.

    These sentences each need two semi-colons.

    ....

    ....

2 marks

Ssssemi-colons are ssssimple for Punctuation Pythons.
Tick a box to show how much of a python you are.

Mixed practice

1) Tick the sentence that uses punctuation correctly.

Mum packed everything we needed; four umbrellas, a picnic basket, which was full of all sorts of food, and a frisbee. ☐

Mum packed everything we needed: four umbrellas; a picnic basket, which was full of all sorts of food; and a frisbee. ☐

Mum packed everything we needed: four umbrellas; a picnic basket; which was full of all sorts of food, and a frisbee. ☐

Now have a go at these questions to see what you've learned in this section.

2) Each of these sentences is missing either a colon or a semi-colon.
Put the correct punctuation mark in the box provided.

There are three things I can't live without ☐ friendship, music and cheese.

I was carrying a rake (with no handle) ☐ a heavy, brown bag; and a spade.

For breakfast, I eat muesli, which I have with milk; a few slices of banana ☐
and some fresh apple juice.

_____
2 marks

3) The box below contains three sentences that are jumbled up. Draw a line from
the beginning of each sentence to the end, going through a colon or a semi-colon.

Dorothy was a farmer	There's someone waiting for you	The crown was very sparkly
;	:	;
her brother was a mechanic.	the king loved wearing it.	your uncle Robert.

_____
2 marks

Mixed practice

4) Some of the punctuation in these sentences is wrong. Rewrite the sentences using colons and semi-colons correctly.

My horse eats hay my snake: eats mice.

My horse eats hay; my snake eats mice.

....

They went to the cinema: the film they saw was terrible.

....

....

Lily was reading; a book Oliver was riding his bike.

....

....

Anton bumped into the person he least expected; his own brother.

....

....

_____
2 marks

5) Write in the **three** semi-colons that are missing in this passage.

My aunt is a champion tap dancer. She started tap dancing when she was a little girl she's now been tap dancing for over thirty years. She's been to competitions in cities all around the world, including Paris, where she won first prize Tokyo which is in Japan and London, where she lives.

_____
2 marks

Punctuation Pythons know just about everything there is to know about colons and semi-colons. How did you get on?

Section 5 — Colons and Semi-Colons

Mixed practice

Warm Up

It's time to test everything you've learned. Start with this warm up question.

1)   Complete each of these sentences by adding one of the punctuation marks below. Only use each punctuation mark once.

| ” | ! | . | ? | , |

"There's no porridge left, ⬚ **Elsie said.**

While it was snowing ⬚ **Rupert went for a walk.**

"Do you like my new shoes ⬚ **" asked the spider.**

A wildebeest is a type of antelope ⬚

"Hold onto my hand ⬚ **" Brandon cried.**

Now have a go at this mix of questions covering topics from across the book.

2)   Draw lines to match each sentence to the correct term.

Why are there so many wasps?		statement
What a big cake that is!		exclamation
Don't forget to wear your gloves.		question
I was born in the year 2009.		command

2 marks

3)   This passage is missing **three** commas.
Add the missing commas in the right places.

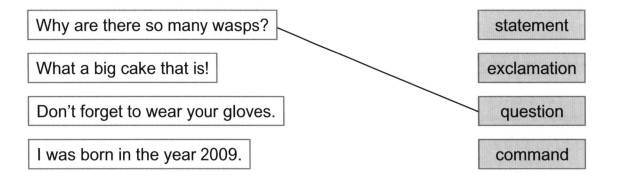

Last night I ate some cheese four oranges and a large grapefruit. When I woke up this morning I felt very ill.

2 marks

Mixed practice

4) Each of these sentences has either a dash or a comma that isn't needed.
    Cross out the punctuation mark that isn't needed in each sentence.

    The England cricket captain — playing his final game — scored fifty — runs.

    My grandmother, who is ninety years old, came to watch me, play football.

    No one — not even the tall people — could see — over the fence.

    The field, which is just behind my house, was full of fluffy, sheep.

    _____
    2 marks

5) The colons and semi-colons are missing from these sentences. Put either
    a colon or a semi-colon in each box so that the sentences make sense.

    Aadhya found three items in the box ☐ an old book, a toy train and a watch.

    There's just one thing left for us to do ☐ celebrate.

    It rained all day ☐ I was glad I brought my coat.

    Please buy these things ☐ a bread roll, which you should get from the local
    bakery ☐ two cartons of fresh orange juice ☐ and a bag of grapes.

    _____
    2 marks

6) Underline the punctuation errors in these sentences.
    There are **two** errors in each sentence.

    <u>Were</u> going to buy <u>twenty five</u> burgers.

    I'm surprised that your'e an ex teacher.

    The brown-dog was chasing it's tail.

    Its strange that weve both got sore feet.

    Theyre still waiting for me to re-ply to their message.

    _____
    2 marks

Mixed practice

7) All the capital letters and apostrophes are missing from these sentences. Rewrite each sentence so that it is punctuated correctly.

There are three mistakes in each sentence.

martin couldnt go to greece because his flight was cancelled.

Martin couldn't go to Greece because his flight was cancelled.

ive never seen a mouses tail.

....

jamaal said, "theyre arriving soon."

....

dr hillary always forgets peoples names.

....

2 marks

8) Each of these sentences is missing one punctuation mark. Put the correct punctuation mark in each box.

My neighbours ☐ Louise and Cheryl) are having a barbecue.

How did you know my name ☐

After the witch made her potion ☐ she cast a spell.

A few months ago ☐ I think it was in May — I saw a shooting star.

The astronaut, who was highly trained ☐ landed the spaceship safely.

"What a hideous monster that is! ☐ cried Alex.

2 marks

Punctuation Pythons are confident about using the right punctuation marks, but are you? Tick one of the boxes.

Proofreading

| Warm Up |

Proofreading is all about reading something you've written very carefully to spot any mistakes. In this section, you're just looking for punctuation errors.

1) Each of these sentences contains **two** punctuation errors.
   Circle the errors, then rewrite each sentence, correcting the mistakes.

   In the afternoon — we met Dennis my uncle).

   ....

   Juan had three hobbies; dancing, tennis; and reading.

   ....

   "I cant stop eating peas"! Jess cried.

   ....

Now try spotting the mistakes in these passages.

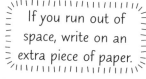

If you run out of space, write on an extra piece of paper.

2) Circle the **eight** punctuation errors in this passage.
   Then rewrite the passage underneath, correcting the mistakes.

   > Mayor Sallys' garden is famous in our town. The garden isn't big (it's smaller than ours, but its full of interesting things There's a group of twenty four robotic gnomes that dance around the patio: an enormous-fountain, which flows with liquid chocolate; and a hedge in the shape of a dinosaur?

   ....

   ....

   ....

   ....

   ....

   4 marks

Section 6 — Mixed Practice

Proofreading

3) Circle the **twelve** punctuation errors in this passage.
Then rewrite the passage underneath, correcting the mistakes.

If you run out of space, write on an extra piece of paper.

One day; Mandy was sitting on the sofa with her puppy who was called henry) on her lap, when she noticed that it was raining outside.

"What awful weather weve been having?" Mandy said to herself.

"I agree. Its so wet out there," came a strange voice from her lap

Mandy was stunned: Henry had just spoken! She lifted him up and turned the long eared pup towards her.

Did you just speak!" Mandy whispered.

Mandy looked at her dog uncertainly; Henry stared back at her and said nothing.

"How silly I am! of course you didn't speak — youre a dog," Mandy said.

Henry winked at her.

....

....

....

....

....

....

....

....

6 marks

Punctuation Pythons are super skilled at spotting mistakes.
Did you find all the mistakes? Tick one of the boxes.

Glossary

COMMON PUNCTUATION MARKS

Apostrophes — show **missing letters** and **belonging**. `'`

Brackets — **separate extra information** in a sentence. `( )`

Bullet points — **separate** different points in a **list**. `•`

Capital letters — used for **proper nouns** and for **starting** sentences. `A`

Colons — **introduce some lists** and **join sentences**. `:`

Commas — **separate** items in a **list**, separate **extra information** in a sentence and **separate clauses**. `,`

Dashes — **separate extra information** in a sentence. `—`

Exclamation marks — show **strong feeling** or **commands**. `!`

Full stops — show where **sentences end**. `.`

Hyphens — **link words** or parts of words to make the meaning clear. `-`

Inverted commas (speech marks) — show **direct speech**. `" "`

Question marks — used at the **end** of **questions**. `?`

Semi-colons — **separate lists** of **longer things** and **join sentences**. `;`

USEFUL WORDS

Command — A **sentence** that **tells** somebody to **do something**.

Direct speech — The **actual words** that are **said** by someone.

Exclamation — **A sentence** that starts with 'what' or 'how' and shows **strong emotion**.

Parenthesis — **Extra information** in a sentence separated by a pair of **commas**, **brackets** or **dashes**. The sentence should make sense if the parenthesis is left out.

Question — A **sentence** that **asks something**.

Reported speech — What someone has said, but **not in their own words**.

Statement — A **sentence** that **gives information**.

Scoresheet

Fill in your scores below, then add them up to find your total marks.

Section 1	Score
Capital letters and full stops	/ 10
Exclamation marks and question marks	/ 9
Sentences	/ 16
Mixed practice	/ 8
Total for Section 1	**/ 43**

Section 2	Score
Apostrophes	/ 22
Inverted commas	/ 19
Mixed practice	/ 7
Total for Section 2	**/ 48**

Section 3	Score
Commas	/ 20
Mixed practice	/ 9
Total for Section 3	**/ 29**

Section 4	Score
Brackets for extra information	/ 9
Dashes for extra information	/ 4
Single dashes and bullet points	/ 3
Hyphens	/ 7
Mixed practice	/ 8
Total for Section 4	**/ 31**

Section 5	Score
Colons	/ 8
Semi-colons	/ 7
Mixed practice	/ 8
Total for Section 5	**/ 23**

Section 6	Score
Mixed practice	/ 14
Proofreading	/ 10
Total for Section 6	**/ 24**

Total for Book	198

Look at your total score to see how you're doing and where you need more practice:

0 – 120 — You've made a good start. Revise punctuation and then have another go.

121 – 170 — You're doing well. Have another look at any sections you're struggling with.

171 – 198 — You're doing really well. Give yourself a pat on the back.

This page may be photocopied